GuestSpot

SMASH HITS
Playalong *for* Violin

WISE PUBLICATIONS
London/New York/Paris/Sydney/Copenhagen/Madrid/Tokyo

Exclusive Distributors:
Music Sales Limited
8/9 Frith Street, London W1D 3JB, England.
Music Sales Pty Limited
120 Rothschild Avenue, Rosebery, NSW 2018, Australia.

Order No. AM968209
ISBN 0-7119-8582-0
This book © Copyright 2000 by Wise Publications.

Music arranged by Paul Honey.
Music processed by Enigma Music Production Services.
Cover photography by George Taylor.
Printed in the United Kingdom by Page Bros., Norwich, Norfolk.

CD produced by Paul Honey.
Instrumental solos by Dermot Crehan.

Your Guarantee of Quality:
As publishers, we strive to produce every book to
the highest commercial standards.
The music has been freshly engraved and the book has been
carefully designed to minimise awkward page turns and
to make playing from it a real pleasure.
Particular care has been given to specifying acid-free, neutral-sized
paper made from pulps which have not been elemental chlorine bleached.
This pulp is from farmed sustainable forests and was
produced with special regard for the environment.
Throughout, the printing and binding have been planned to
ensure a sturdy, attractive publication which should give years of enjoyment.
If your copy fails to meet our high standards,
please inform us and we will gladly replace it.

Music Sales' complete catalogue describes thousands of
titles and is available in full colour sections by subject,
direct from Music Sales Limited.
Please state your areas of interest and send a
cheque/postal order for £1.50 for postage to:
Music Sales Limited, Newmarket Road, Bury St. Edmunds, Suffolk IP33 3YB.

www.musicsales.com

Breathless

Words & Music by R.J Lange, Andrea Corr, Caroline Corr, Sharon Corr & Jim Corr

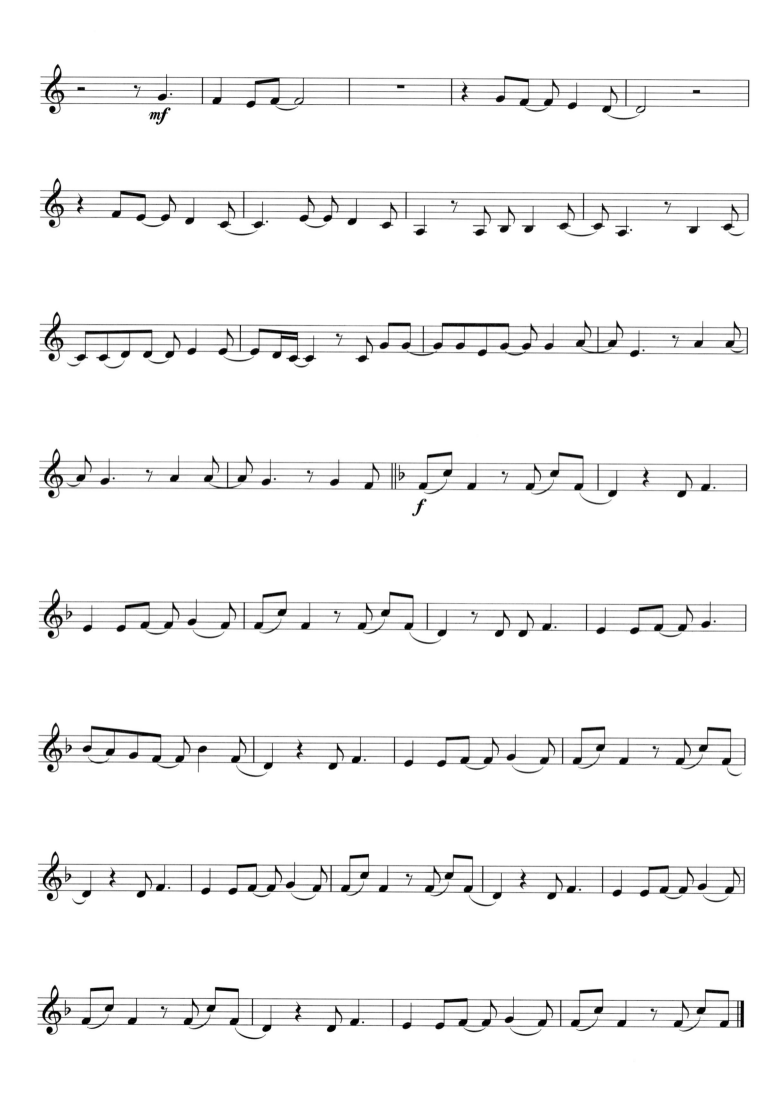

American Pie

Words & Music by Don McLean

Desert Rose

Words & Music by Sting

Reach

Words & Music by Cathy Dennis & Andrew Todd

Step into the spotlight with...

GUEST SPOT

...and playalong *with* the

specially recorded backing tracks

A great book and CD series,
each title available in arrangements for
**FLUTE, CLARINET, ALTO SAXOPHONE,
TENOR SAXOPHONE*, TRUMPET* and VIOLIN***

Pull Out

Now you can
own *professional*

when you play all these

for Clarinet, Flute, Alto Saxophone

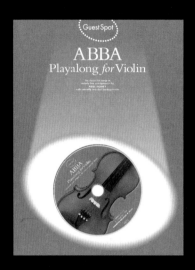

The *essential* book & CD series...

From Jazz, Blues and Swing to Ballads,
Showstoppers, Film and TV Themes, here
are all your favourite Chart Hits and more!
Check out the special editions featuring legends
of pop, **Abba** and **The Beatles**.

The Music Book...

Top line arrangements for 10 songs,
plus a fingering guide for wind instruments.

The CD...

Hear full performance versions of all the songs.
Then play along with the recorded accompaniments.

ABBA
Includes:
Dancing Queen
Fernando
Mamma Mia
Waterloo

AM960905 Clarinet
AM960894 Flute
AM960916 Alto Saxophone
AM960927 Violin

BALLADS
Includes:
Candle In The Wind
Imagine
Killing Me Softly With His Song
Wonderful Tonight

AM941787 Clarinet
AM941798 Flute
AM941809 Alto Saxophone

THE BEATLES
Includes:
All You Need Is Love
Hey Jude
Lady Madonna
Yesterday

NO90682 Clarinet
NO90683 Flute
NO90684 Alto Saxophone

CHRISTMAS
Includes:
Frosty The Snowman
Have Yourself A Merry Little
   Christmas
Mary's Boy Child
Winter Wonderland

AM950400 Clarinet
AM950411 Flute
AM950422 Alto Saxophone

have your very backing band...

great melody line arrangements
Tenor Saxophone*, Trumpet* and Violin*

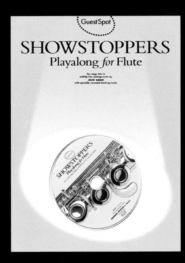

CLASSIC BLUES

Includes:
Fever
Harlem Nocturne
Moonglow
Round Midnight

AM941743 Clarinet
AM941754 Flute
AM941765 Alto Saxophone

CLASSICS

Includes:
Air On The 'G' String - Bach
Jupiter (from The Planets Suite) - Holst
Ode To Joy (Theme from Symphony No.9 'Choral') - Beethoven
Swan Lake (Theme) - Tchaikovsky.

AM955537 Clarinet
AM955548 Flute
AM955560 Violin

FILM THEMES

Includes:
Circle Of Life (The Lion King)
Love Is All Around (Four Weddings & A Funeral)
Moon River (Breakfast At Tiffany's)
You Must Love Me (Evita)

AM941864 Clarinet
AM941875 Flute
AM941886 Alto Saxophone

JAZZ

Includes:
Fly Me To The Moon
Opus One
Satin Doll
Straight No Chaser

AM941700 Clarinet
AM941710 Flute
AM941721 Alto Saxophone

NINETIES HITS

Includes:
Falling Into You (Celine Dion)
Never Ever (All Saints)
Tears In Heaven (Eric Clapton)
2 Become 1 (Spice Girls)

AM952853 Clarinet
AM952864 Flute
AM952875 Alto Saxophone

No.1 HITS

Includes:
A Whiter Shade Of Pale (Procol Harum)
Every Breath You Take (The Police)
No Matter What (Boyzone)
Unchained Melody (The Righteous Brothers).

AM955603 Clarinet
AM955614 Flute
AM955625 Alto Saxophone
AM959530 Violin

SHOWSTOPPERS

Includes:
Big Spender (Sweet Charity)
Bring Him Home (Les Misérables)
I Know Him So Well (Chess)
Somewhere (West Side Story)

AM941820 Clarinet
AM941831 Flute
AM941842 Alto Saxophone

SWING

Includes:
I'm Getting Sentimental Over You
Is You Is Or Is You Ain't My Baby?
Perdido
Tuxedo Junction

AM949377 Clarinet
AM960575 Trumpet
AM949399 Alto Saxophone
AM959618 Tenor Saxophone

TV THEMES

Includes:
Black Adder
Home And Away
London's Burning
Star Trek

AM941908 Clarinet
AM941919 Flute
AM941920 Alto Saxophone

* Selected titles only

Sample the *whole* series of *Guest Spot* with these special double CD bumper compilations...

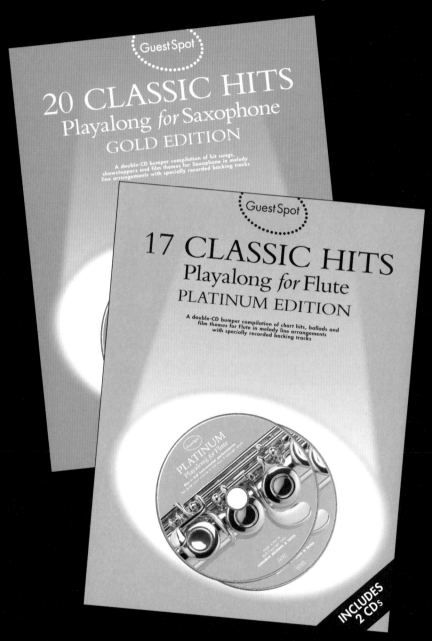

GUEST SPOT GOLD

Twenty all-time Hit Songs, Showstoppers and Film Themes

Includes:
A Whiter Shade Of Pale (Procol Harum)
Bridge Over Troubled Water
   (Simon & Garfunkel)
Don't Cry For Me Argentina (from Evita)
Yesterday (The Beatles)
Where Do I Begin (Theme from Love Story)
Words (Boyzone)
Yesterday (The Beatles)

AM960729 Clarinet
AM960718 Flute
AM960730 Alto Saxophone

GUEST SPOT PLATINUM

Seventeen greatest Chart Hits, Ballads and Film Themes

Includes:
Circle Of Life (from The Lion King)
Candle In The Wind (Elton John)
Dancing Queen (Abba)
Falling Into You (Celine Dion)
I Believe I Can Fly (R. Kelly)
Take My Breath Away (Berlin)
Torn (Natalie Imbruglia

AM960751 Clarinet
AM960740 Flute
AM960762 Alto Saxophone

PUB04626

Repeat and fade

I Have A Dream

Words & Music by Benny Andersson & Björn Ulvaeus

Oops!... I Did It Again

Words & Music by Max Martin & Rami Yacoub

Pure Shores

Words & Music by William Orbit, Shaznay Lewis & Susannah Melvoin

Repeat to fade

Natural Blues

Words & Music by Vera Hall
Arranged by Moby
'Natural Blues' is based on the song 'Trouble So Hard' (Words & Music by Vera Hall)

Moderately

25

She's The One

Words & Music by Karl Wallinger

Rise

Words & Music by Bob Dylan, Gabrielle, Ferdy Unger-Hamilton & Ollie Dagois

Rather slow

Repeat to fade